Through The Eyes of The Eagle

written by Georgia Perez

illustrated by Patrick Rolo & Lisa A. Fifield

The Story of the Eagle Books

Diabetes Prevention Stories for Native American Children

Stories can allow the positive power of words to create a new empowering vision of the future and reshape the way one thinks about disease.

Janette Carter, Georgia Perez, Susan Gilliland (1999). Communicating through stories: Experience of the Native American Diabetes Project. Diabetes Educator, 25, 179-187

Traditionally, stories were told in winter by Native Americans to pass on their history, traditions, and culture to future generations because Native languages were only spoken, not written. The stories in the Eagle Books came from a recurring dream I had and from the dreams of many Native Indian communities whose members wanted to make life better for people dealing with diabetes.

In 1989, I met a wonderful physician, Dr. Janette Carter. In 1994, I started to work with her to develop a diabetes education curriculum funded by the National Institutes of Health. During the development of the curriculum, I dreamed of being visited by an eagle. The eagle was showing me how life for Native Americans used to be and what Native people can do to prevent diabetes now.

Dr. Carter expressed a need for the diabetes curriculum to be more culturally tailored for the population that we were trying to reach. I told her about the dream that I had been having. It was then that the original story, "Through the Eyes of the Eagle," was written and woven throughout our first curriculum.

Published by the U.S. Department of Health and Human Services, Centers for Disease Control and Prevention, Division of Diabetes Translation, National Diabetes Prevention Center

The story broke down barriers that people had about health and diabetes. When we began with the story and then talked about diabetes, we found that the children listened intently. They were eager to take the information back to their parents and talk about what they had learned in school that day. It became a future dream to write a series of children's books to help them learn how important it is to have healthy eating and physical activity in their lives. In July 2001, Janette Carter passed away and never had an opportunity to see this dream become reality. But it did. She would be glad.

In 2002, the Native Diabetes Wellness Program (formerly the National Diabetes Prevention Center), Centers for Disease Control and Prevention, formed partnerships with the New Mexico State Diabetes Prevention and Control Program and the Office of Native American Diabetes Program at the University of New Mexico to plan for the series of children's books. These books would contain healthy lifestyle messages to help children as well as family and community members begin making positive changes in their lives. The underlying messages would be to prevent obesity and diabetes.

The partnerships have expanded even more broadly to include book illustrators Patrick Rolo and Lisa A. Fifield, Native Americans from Minnetonka, Minnesota; Westat, in Atlanta, Georgia; the Indian Health Service, Division of Diabetes Treatment and Prevention, based in Albuquerque, New Mexico; and the Tribal Leaders Diabetes Committee, represented by leaders across the country. Partners and communities are involved from all directions: north, south, east, and west.

"Through the Eyes of the Eagle," is the first story in a four book set. Other books in the set are "Knees Lifted High", "Plate Full of Color" and "Tricky Treats"

-Georgia Perez

A young Indian boy named Rain That Dances lived in a small Indian village. The village was near the foot of a high mountain. The big city was not too far away.

Rain That Dances was a happy little boy.
He liked to play with his friends.

He also liked to sing and dance
with the men in the village.

On this beautiful day with the sky so blue, Rain That Dances was fishing along a small stream near his home. As he waited for the fish to bite, he saw a great bald eagle.

The eagle was resting on an old tree stump not far from where he sat. He had never seen this great bird so close.

Now eagles always fly away when a person comes too close. But for some reason, this great bird just stayed where he was as Rain That Dances came close to the bird. Rain That Dances thought the eagle was hurt and could not fly away. As he got closer, Rain That Dances saw the bird was not hurt at all.

"Mr. Eagle, what is wrong with you?" Rain That Dances said out loud. There must be something else wrong with the great bird. But he did not know what it was.

"Maybe the eagle will tell me what is wrong," Rain That Dances thought to himself. So he asked the bird again, "What is wrong? Why didn't you fly away when I got close to you?" The eagle looked at the young boy and said, "I am just too tired and sad because of all the things I see as I fly around this great land."

3

Rain That Dances gave the bird a surprised look and asked, "What do you mean? I look around here and it is just beautiful! See, the sun is shining. There are beautiful white clouds in the sky. The river has plenty of fish for you to eat, even though the fish won't bite my fishhook. So there is nothing to be sad about."

"You are right! It still looks beautiful!" replied the eagle. But the great bird thought about the stories the Old Wise Eagle used to tell about the things he saw as he flew around. Now things had changed.

The great bird said to Rain That Dances, "As I soar high above the clouds, I see the beauty of the world around me. I see the high peaks of the mountains. I see the valleys below where the water flows in the rivers. I have seen Brother Sun greet each morning of a new day with sunlight. I have seen him say good night as Sister Moon comes to light up the dark sky."

The eagle continued, "The Old Wise Eagle told me stories about the things he saw with each new day. He saw the bear, the buffalo, and the deer. And he saw your people being very active.

Those days were hard. But your people all worked together and shared everything. Hard work and being active was a way of life for everyone."

The eagle told Rain That Dances how years ago, the men worked hard to take care of everyone in the village. They had strong, healthy bodies. They used to hunt for buffalo and deer for this was food for the village.

3

The women worked hard taking care of their families. They planted seeds in Mother Earth to grow the foods that kept their families healthy and strong. The children helped with the chores. But they also played with each other.

"Now as I fly around, I do not see the children playing and moving around like the Old Wise Eagle used to see. Children are also eating foods that are not so good for them. That makes me sad."

"Why should this make you sad?" asked Rain That Dances.

"I am sad because this makes people get sick. They are not as healthy as they can be," said the eagle. "Many of your elders are sick now with a disease they call diabetes.

And the young children will get it too unless they make changes in their lives."

Rain That Dances was quiet for a few minutes as he thought about the people in the village. He thought of the elders who could no longer see the beauty around them because their eyes could not see. He thought about the people who were sick. He also thought of the people who could no longer walk but used wheelchairs to get around.

He had never thought of these things before but now knew the eagle was right.

"You do have reasons to be sad," said Rain That Dances. "Now I am sad too. What can I do to help my people be strong and healthy again?" asked Rain That Dances.

The eagle looked at the young boy and said, "I had a dream last night about this very thing."

Rain That Dances got a big smile on his face, jumped up and asked, "What can I tell them?"

The eagle said, "There is much to tell." You can let your people know that there are things they can do now. They can be healthy and will not have to get diabetes. Going back to some of their traditions, such as the food their ancestors used to eat, becoming active once again, and passing those traditions on to their children are important. In my vision, your people hold the answers. They just have to think back. Now it is getting late and you need to get home. If you come back tomorrow, I will be here. I will tell you more of what your people can do to be healthy and strong again."

Rain That Dances left the eagle. He will come back the next day. He knew what the eagle was telling him was true. He had seen his people get sick with this disease. Now he has a chance to learn what his people can do to be healthy again. He also has a new friend, the great bald eagle.

"Tomorrow is a new day," Rain That Dances said with a smile on his face. He waved goodbye to the eagle. "I'll see you tomorrow and I will bring my best friend with me."

The eagle also wants you to hear what he has to say. Please join Rain That Dances in reading "Knees Lifted High."

This book is the first in a series being developed by the CDC's Native Diabetes Wellness Program (formerly the National Diabetes Prevention Center). We are hoping that, with the support of tribes and organizations, these books can be made available to every American Indian and Alaska Native child as a tool to be integrated with other dedicated efforts at tribal, state, and national levels to prevent diabetes for future generations. If you would like more information or are interested in being one of the sponsors of the book series, please contact the CDC at:

Phone: Toll free
1-800-CDC-INFO (800-232-4636)

TTY: 1-888-232-6348
In English/en Español - 24/7

E-Mail: cdcinfo@cdc.gov

Website: www.cdc.gov/diabetes

Other books in this series:

Book 2: "Knees Lifted High"

Book 3: "Plate Full of Color"

Book 4: "Tricky Treats"